Reasoning and Writing

Level A
Workbook 1

Siegfried Engelmann

Karen Lou Seitz Davis

A Division of The McGraw·Hill Companies

Columbus, Ohio

Cover Credits

(tl, tr) PhotoDisc, (bl) Comstock.

SRA/McGraw-Hill
A Division of The McGraw-Hill Companies

Send all inquiries to:
SRA/McGraw-Hill
8787 Orion Place
Columbus, OH 43240-4027

Printed in the United States of America.

ISBN 0-02-684749-3

5 6 7 8 9 DBH 06 05 04

A.

4 ☑   8 ☐   2 ☐   10 ☐

6 ☐   5 ☐

B.

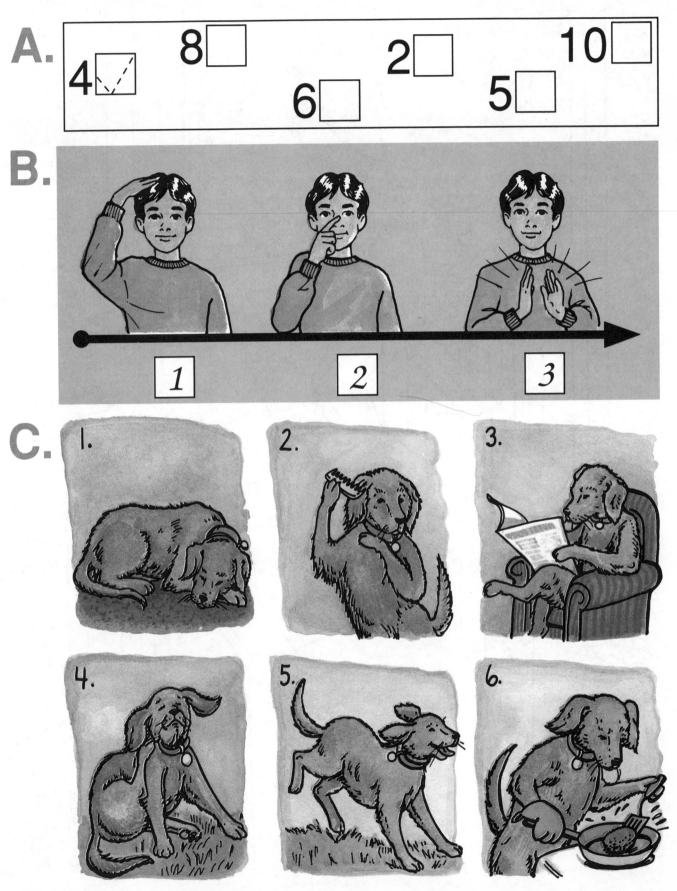

1   2   3

C.

1.   2.   3.

4.   5.   6.

D.

Lesson 2

A. 5 □   ◯ □   7 □   ★ □   ☾ □   🐎 □   3 □

B.

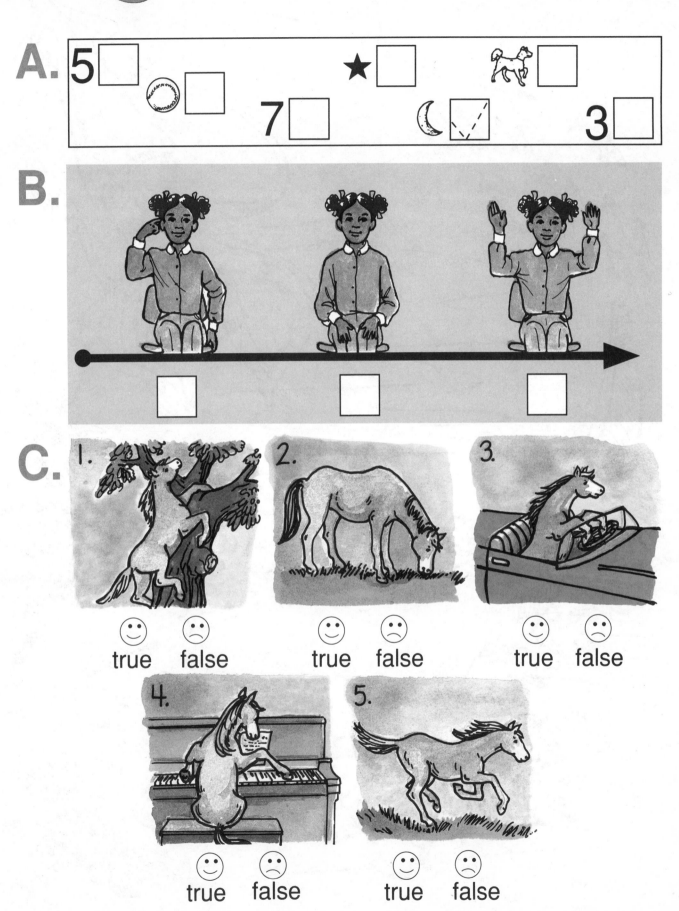

C.

1. 😊 true   🙁 false

2. 😊 true   🙁 false

3. 😊 true   🙁 false

4. 😊 true   🙁 false

5. 😊 true   🙁 false

D.

A. 3☐ 2☐ 🌼☐
9☐ 4☐ 8☐

B.

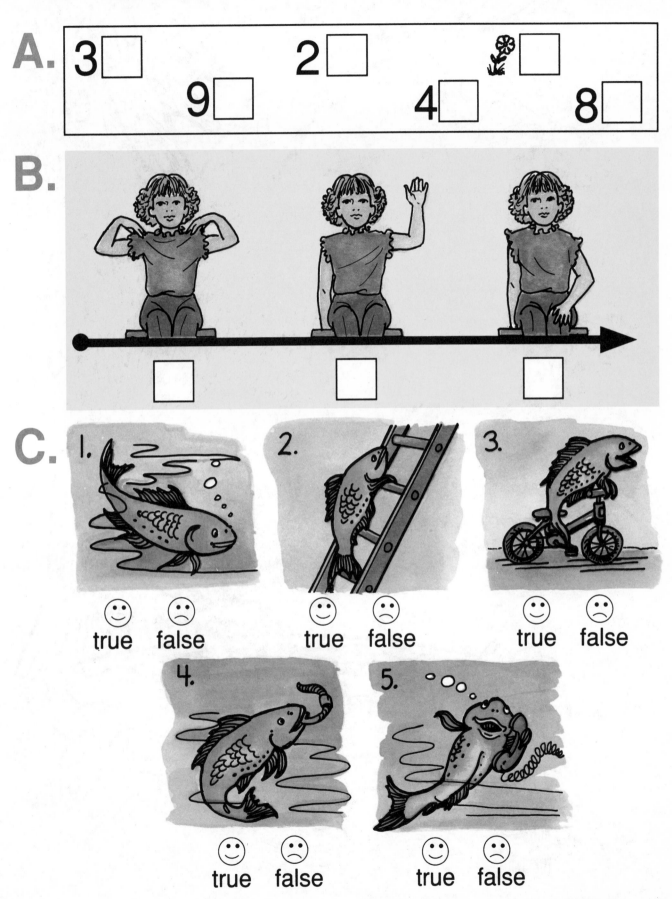

C.

1. true 😊 false 😕

2. true 😊 false 😕

3. true 😊 false 😕

4. true 😊 false 😕

5. true 😊 false 😕

D.

A.

5 ☐   10 ☐   7 ☐   1 ☐   🐱 ☐

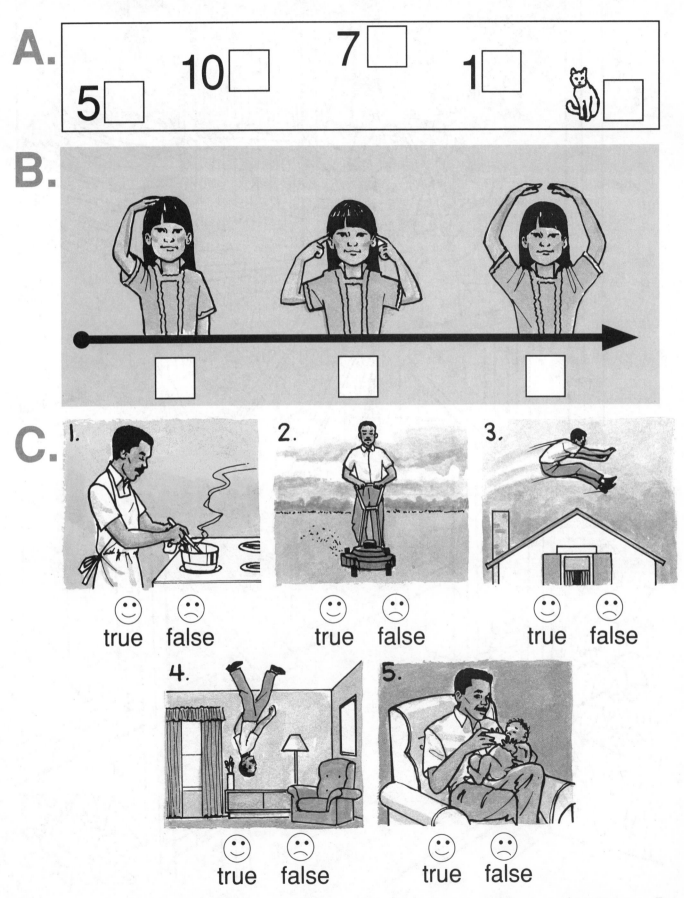

B.

☐   ☐   ☐

C.

1. 🙂 true   🙁 false

2. 🙂 true   🙁 false

3. 🙂 true   🙁 false

4. 🙂 true   🙁 false

5. 🙂 true   🙁 false

D.

Lesson 5

A. 5□   4□   1□   6□
     9□   2□

B.

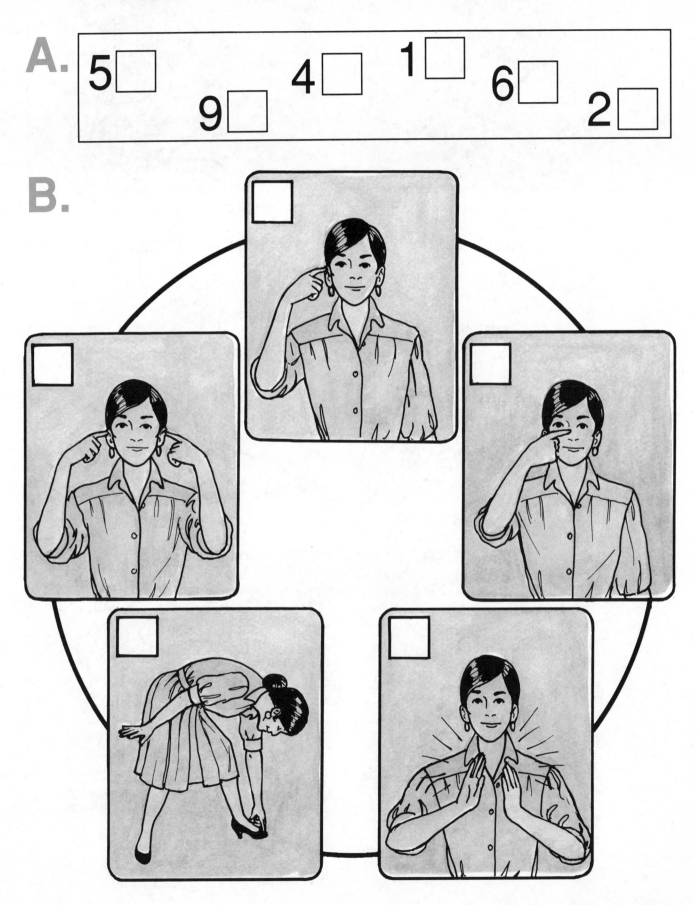

C.

1.

🙂 true   🙁 false

2.

🙂 true   🙁 false

3.

🙂 true   🙁 false

4.

🙂 true   🙁 false

5.

🙂 true   🙁 false

6.

🙂 true   🙁 false

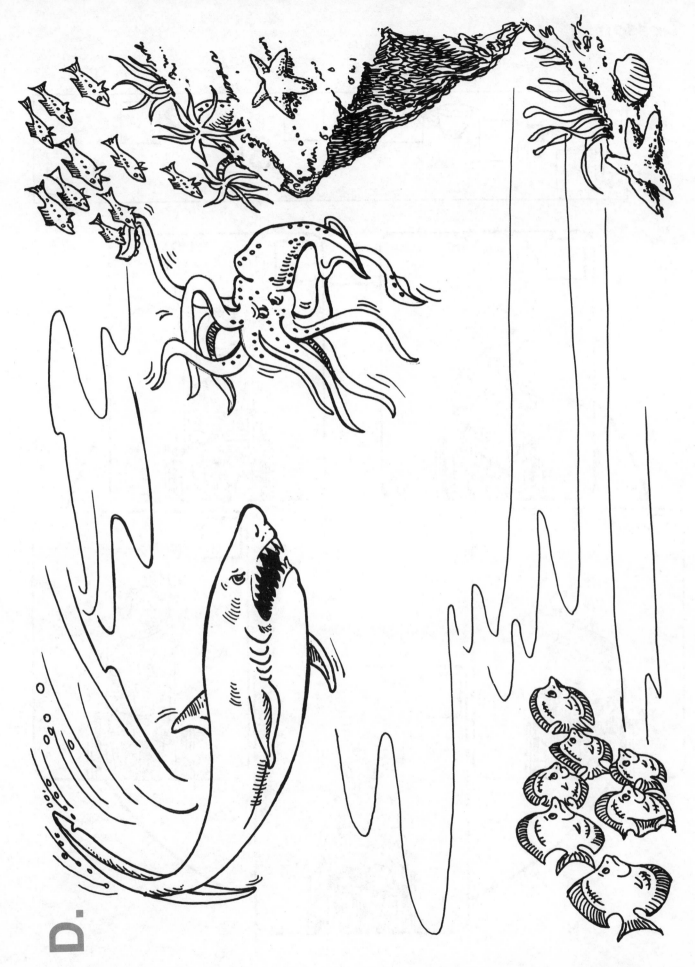

D.

A.

9 ☐   5 ☐   ☕ ☐   6 ☐   3 ☐   2 ☐   1 ☐

B.

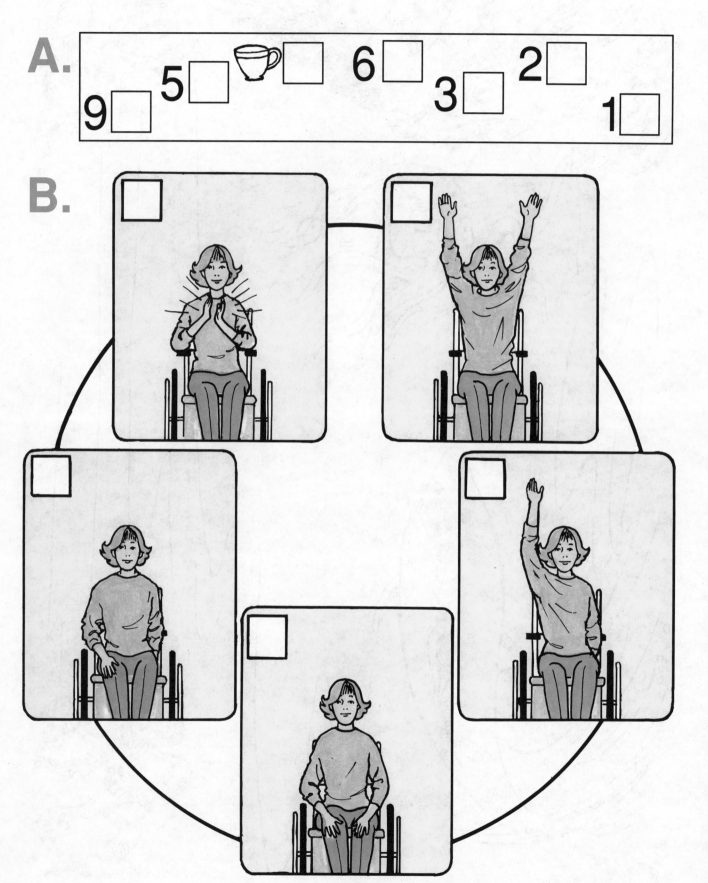

1. true false

2. true false

3. true false

4. true false

5. true false

6. true false

D.

E.

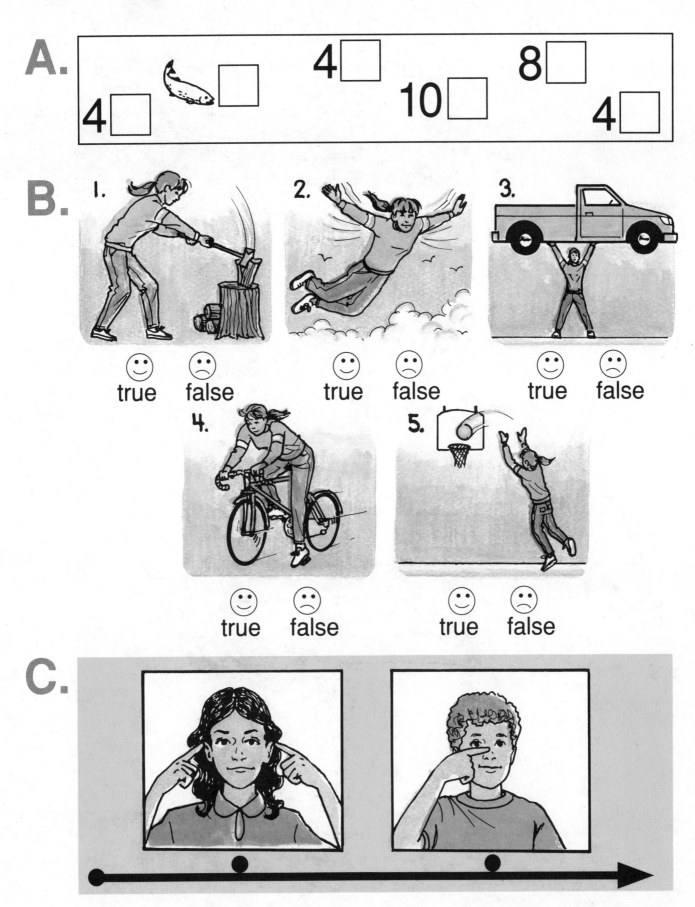

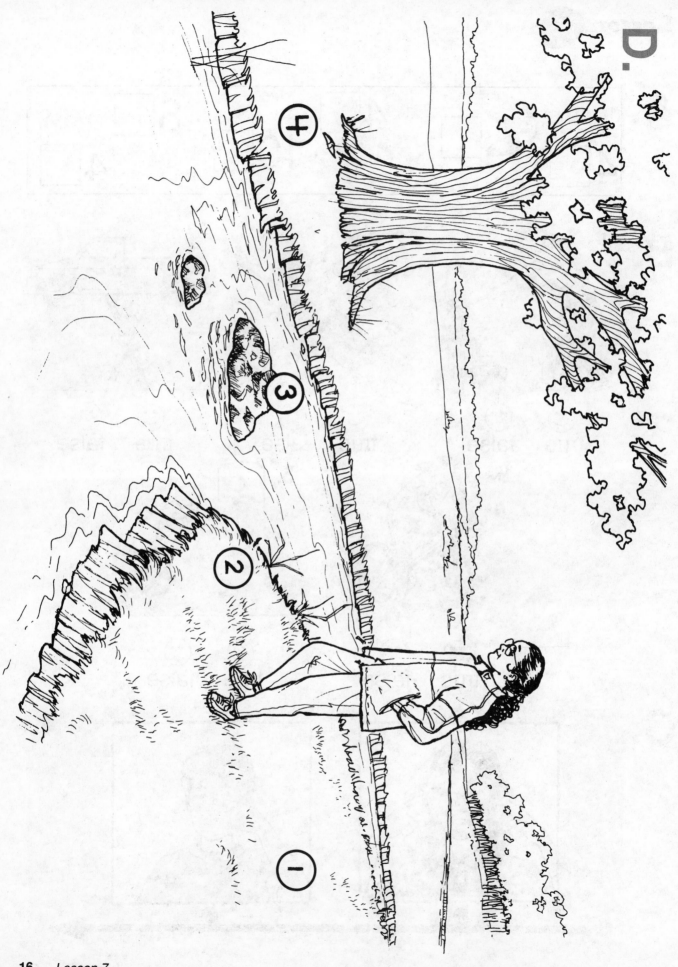

Lesson 8

A.

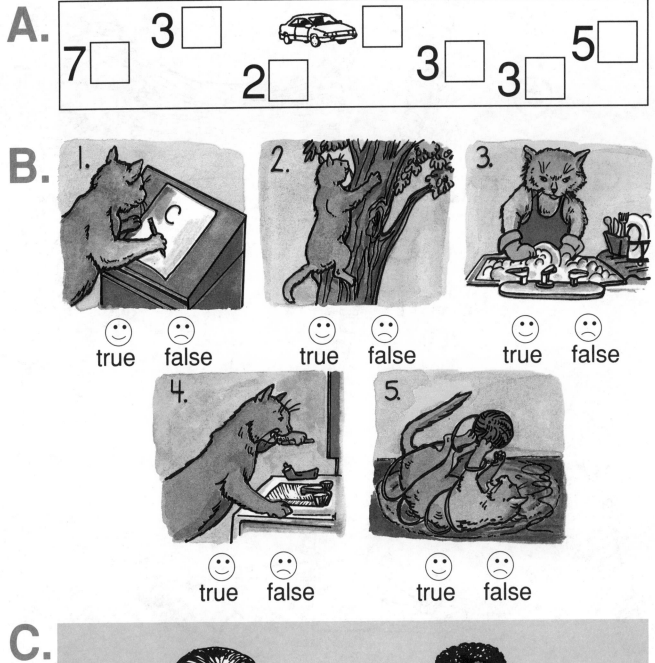

7 ☐ 3 ☐ ☐ 2 ☐ 3 ☐ 3 ☐ 5 ☐

B.

1. ☺ true ☹ false

2. ☺ true ☹ false

3. ☺ true ☹ false

4. ☺ true ☹ false

5. ☺ true ☹ false

C.

5

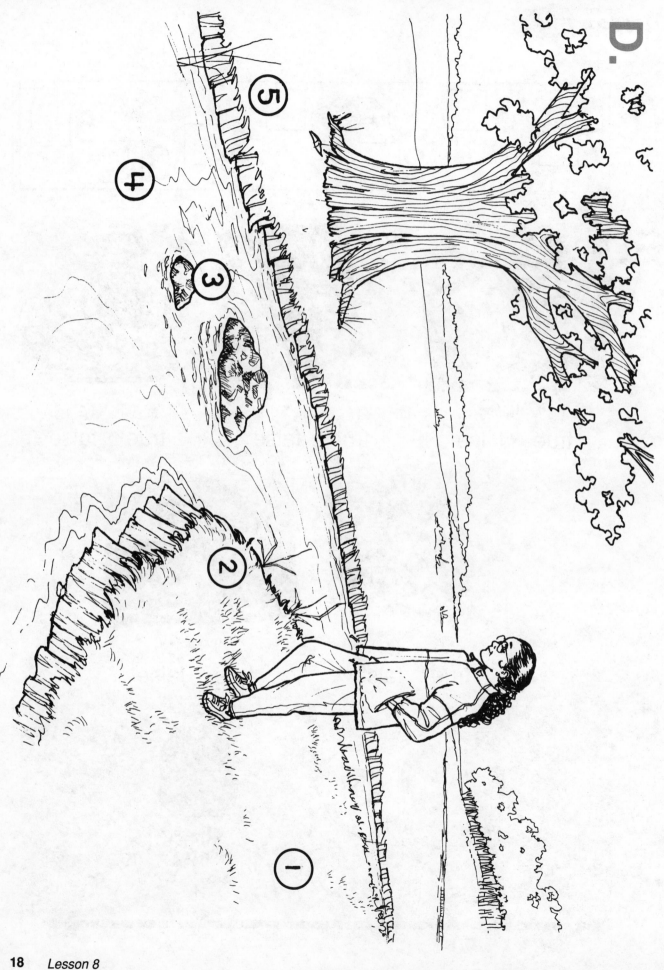

Lesson 9

A.

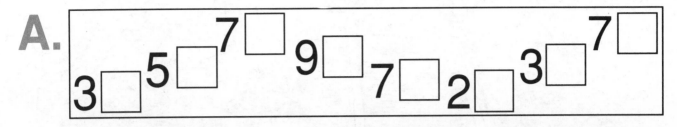

3 □ 5 □ 7 □ 9 □ 7 □ 2 □ 3 □ 7 □

B.

1.　　　　　　　2.　　　　　　　3.

true　false　　　true　false　　　true　false

4.　　　　　　　5.

true　false　　　true　false

C.

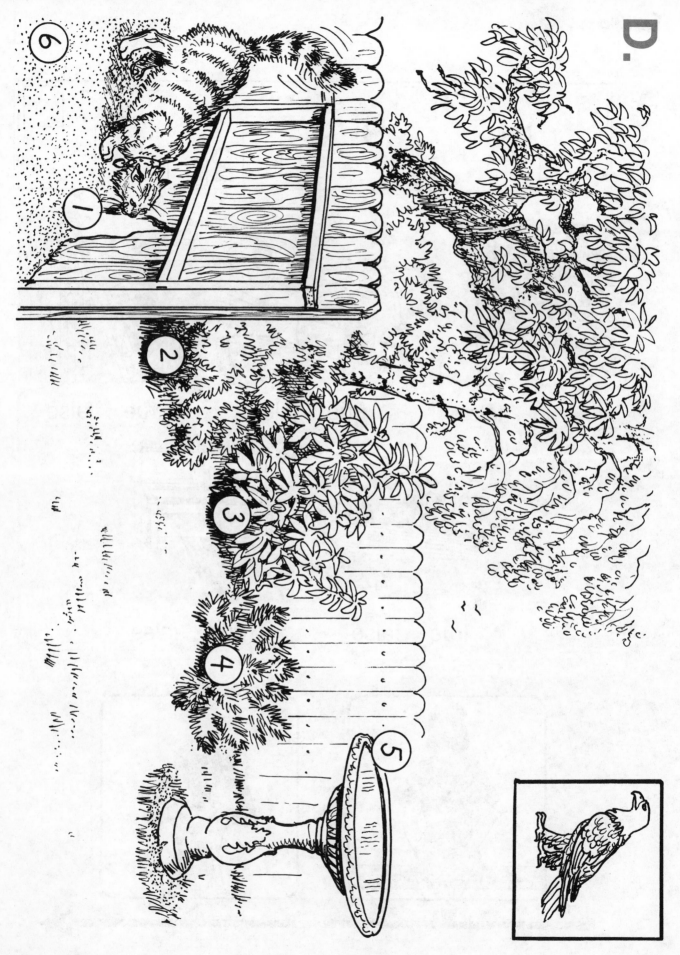

A. 5☐
2☐ 7☐ 5☐ 5☐ 8☐ 5☐

B.

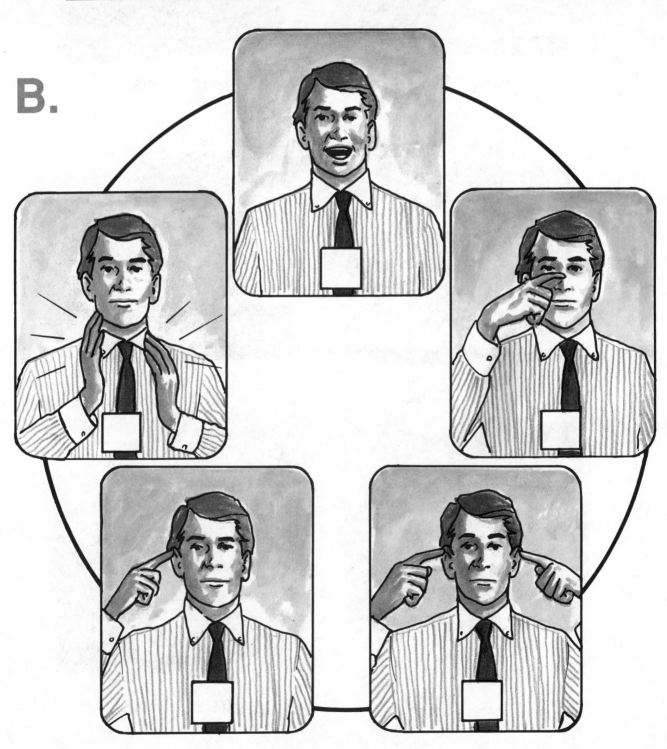

C.

1.

true   false

2.

true   false

3.

true   false

4.

true   false

5.

true   false

6.

true   false

Lesson 11

A.

B.

1. true false

2. true false

3. true false

4. true false

5. true false

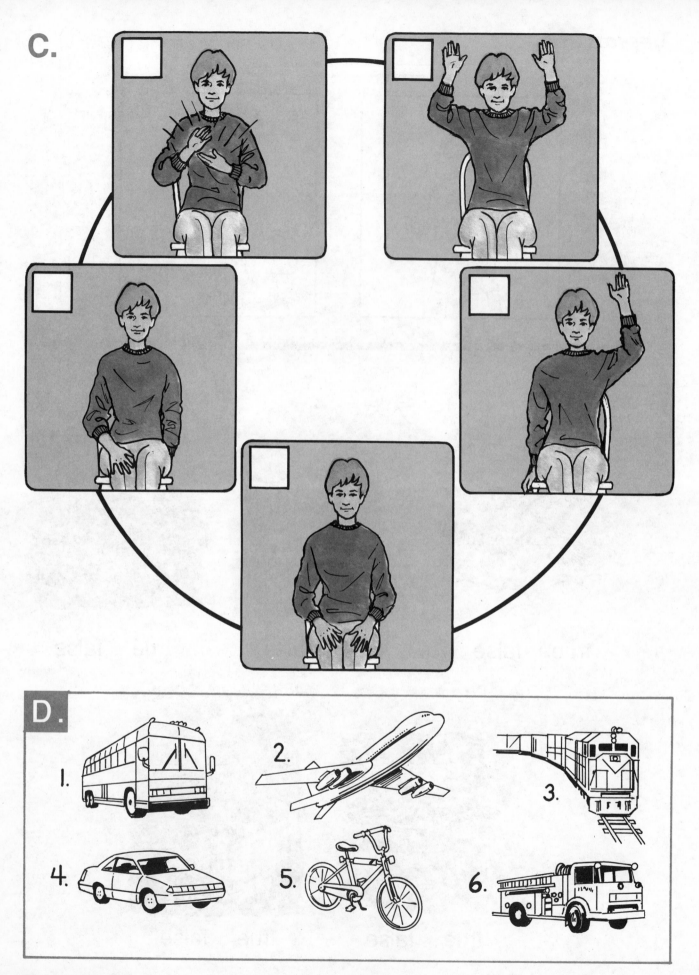

E.

A.

B.

1. true false
2. true false
3. true false
4. true false
5. true false
6. true false

C.

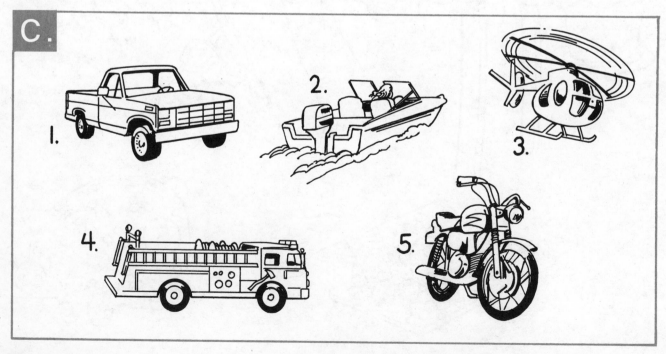

D.

A.

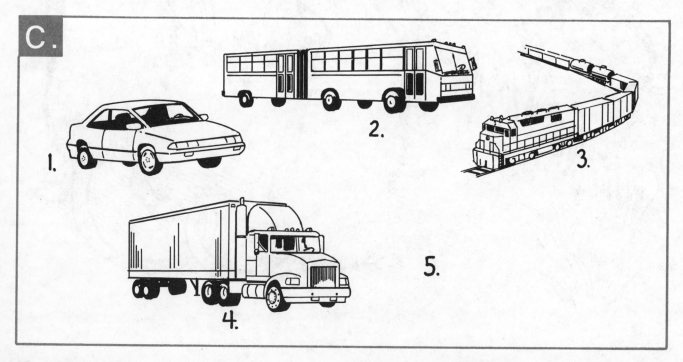

B.

1. true   false
2. true   false
3. true   false
4. true   false
5. true   false
6. true   false

C.

1.

2.

3.

4.

5.

D.

A.

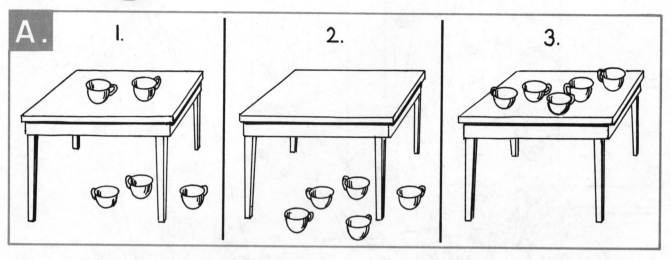

1. 2. 3.

B.

C.

D.

A.

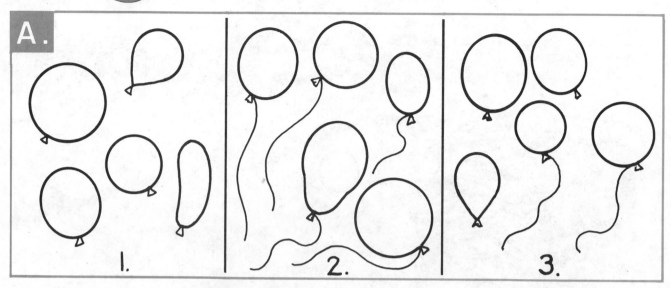

1.

2.

3.

B.

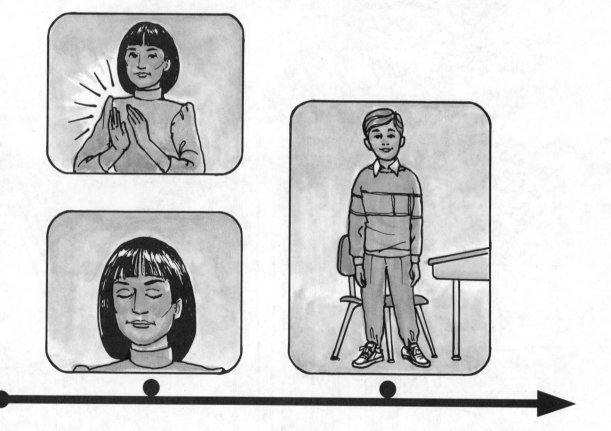

C.

D.

1.

2.

3.

4.

5.

6.

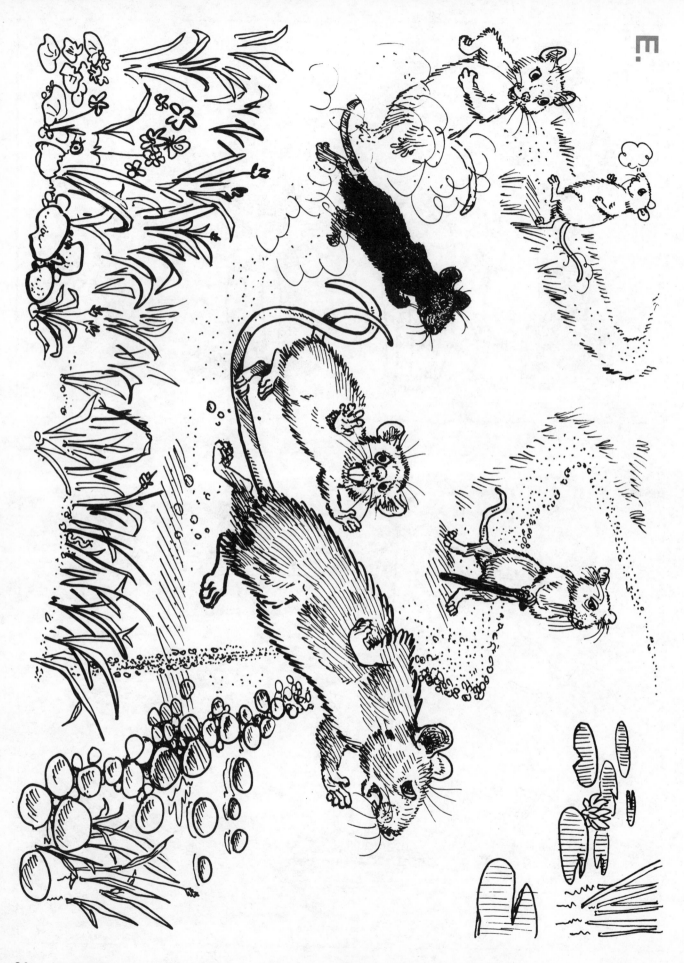

Lesson 16

A.

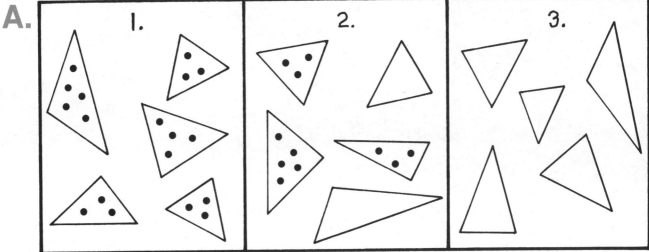

1.   2.   3.

B.

or

C.

1.

2.

3.

4.

D.

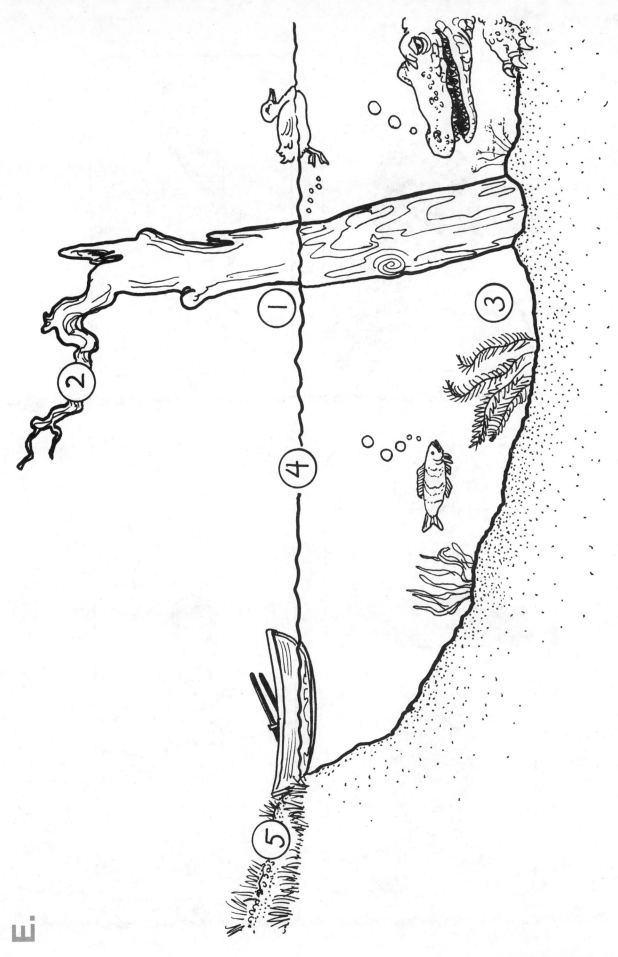

E.

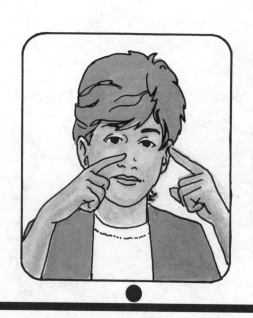

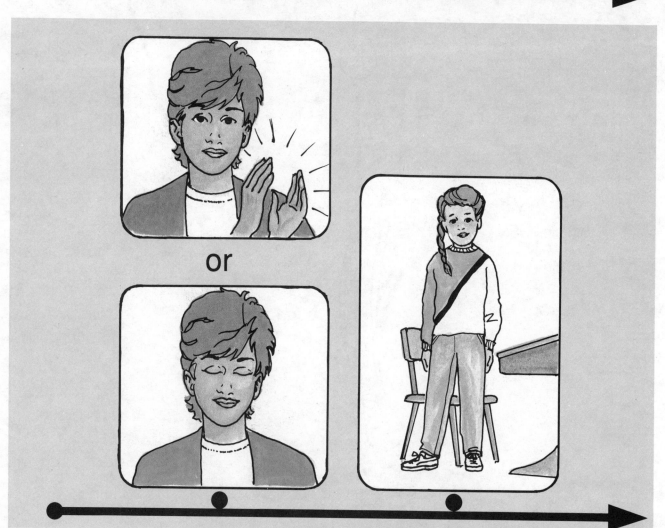

or

B.

1.

2.

3.

4.

5.

C.

1.

2.

3.

4.

Lesson 18

A.

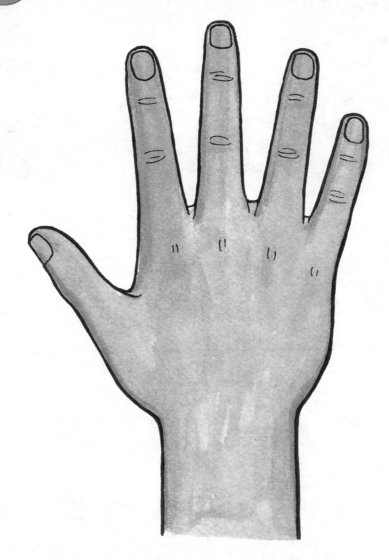

B.

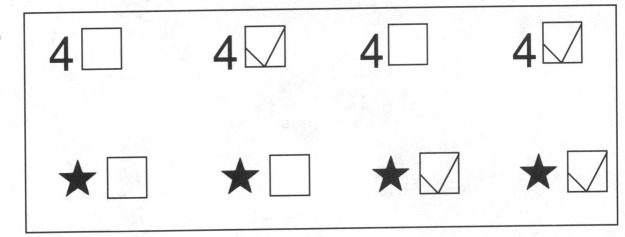

C.

D.

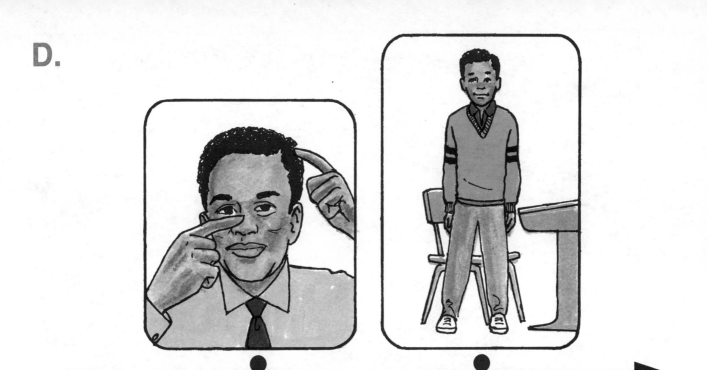

or

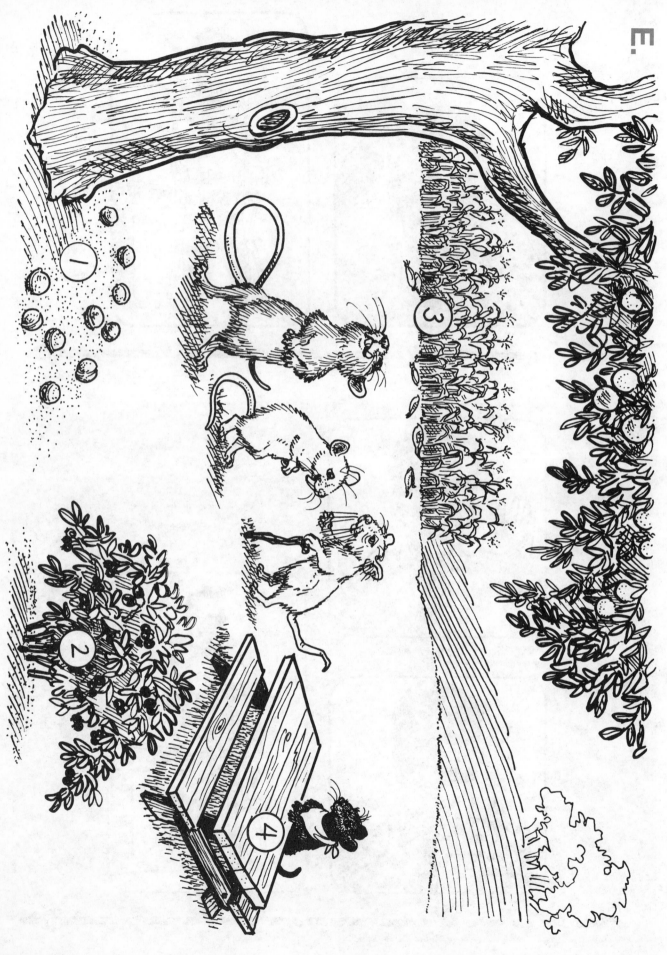

Lesson 19

A.

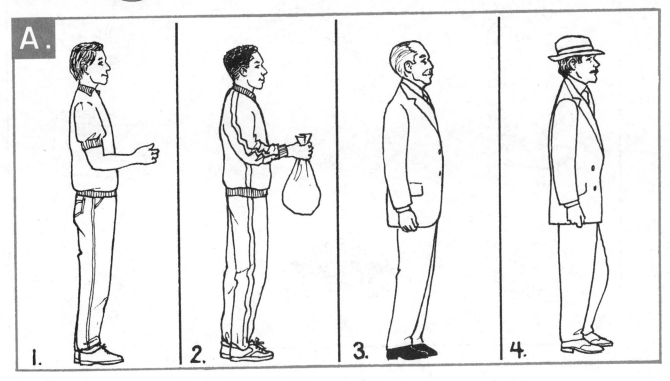

B.

C.

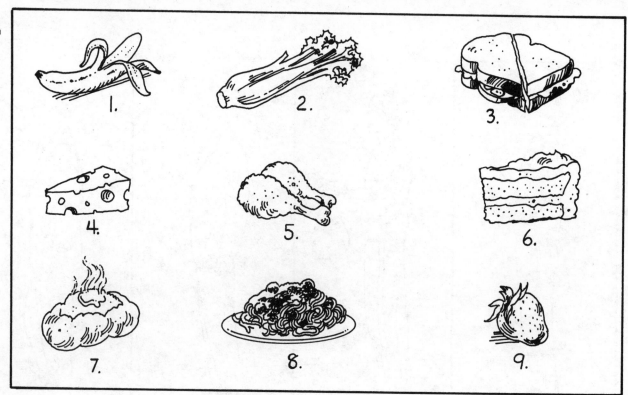

1. 2. 3.

4. 5. 6.

7. 8. 9.

A.

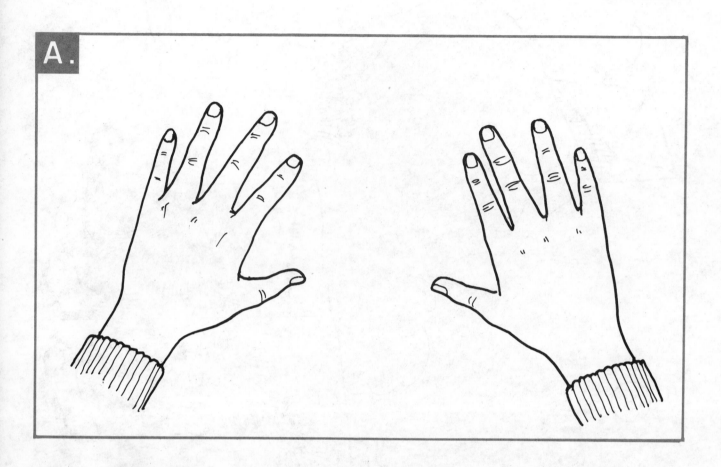

B.

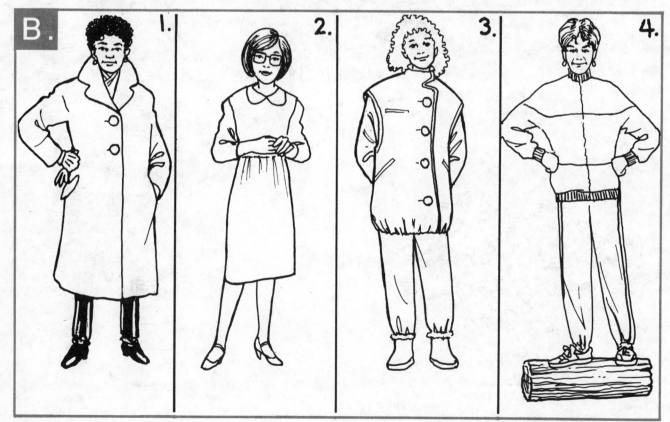

1.

2.

3.

4.

C.

D.

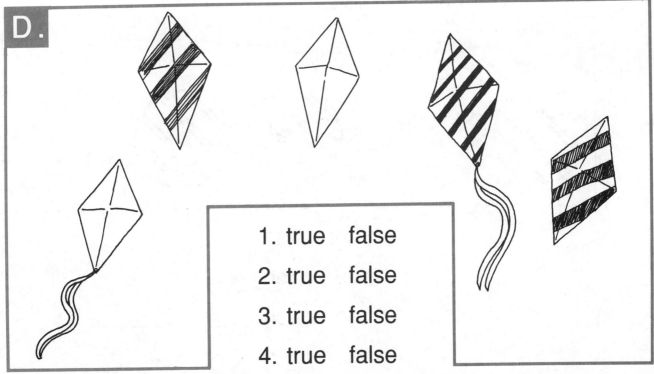

1. true   false
2. true   false
3. true   false
4. true   false

A.

B.

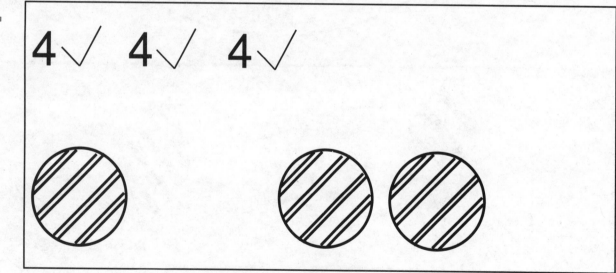

4 ✓   4 ✓   4 ✓

1. true   false

2. true   false

3. true   false

4. true   false

C.

D.

A.

1. true false
2. true false
3. true false
4. true false

B.

C.

A.

③   ③

③

1. true   false
2. true   false
3. true   false
4. true   false

B.

or

C.

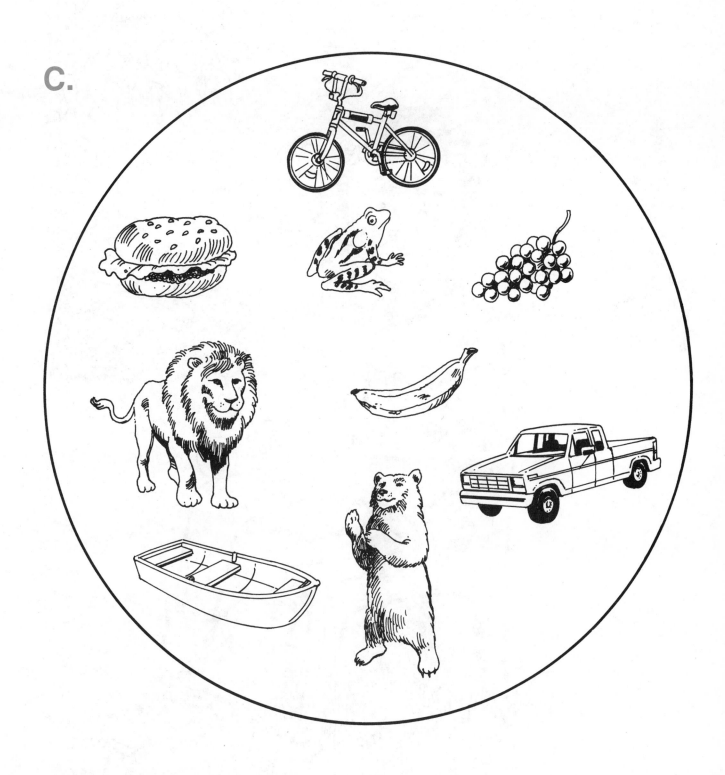

D.

Lesson 24

A.

1. true   false
2. true   false
3. true   false
4. true   false

B.

1.

2.

3.

C.

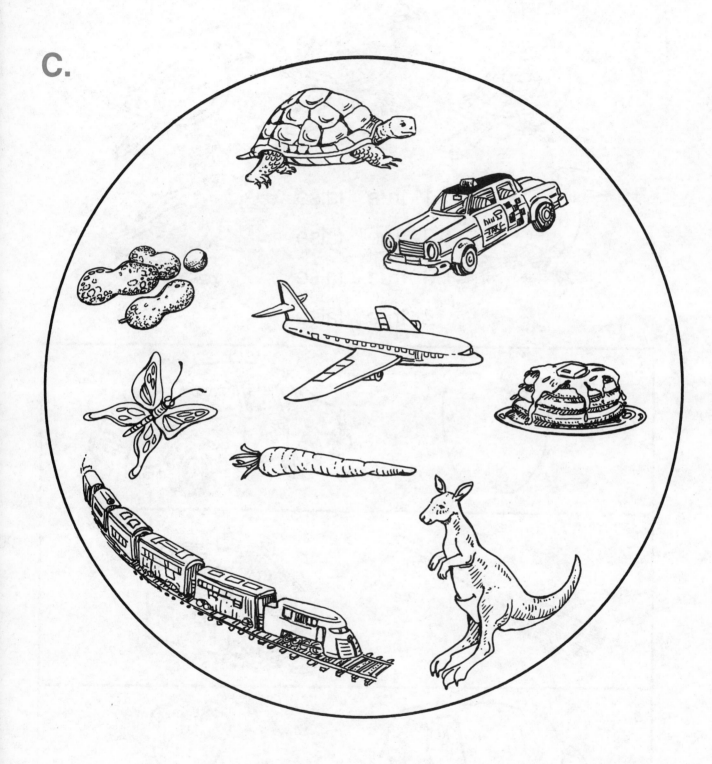

D.

A.

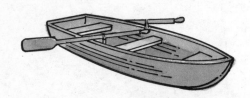

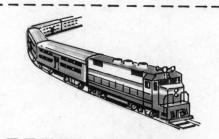

B.

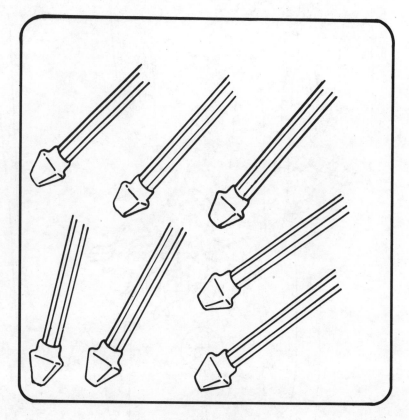

1. true   false

2. true   false

3. true   false

4. true   false

C.

A.

1. true   false

2. true   false

3. true   false

4. true   false

5. true   false

B.

or

C.

A.

B.

C.

1. true false
2. true false
3. true false
4. true false

D.

A.

B.

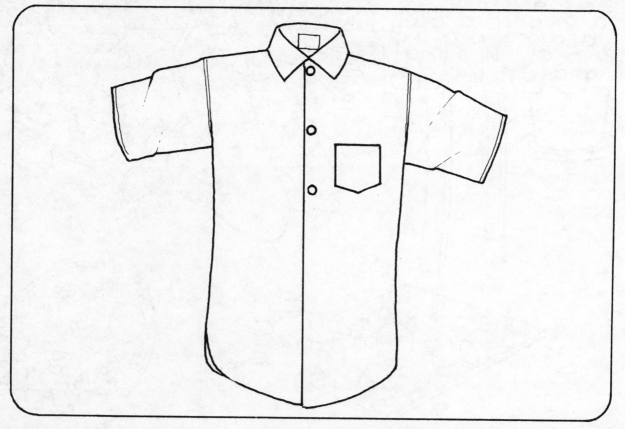

C.

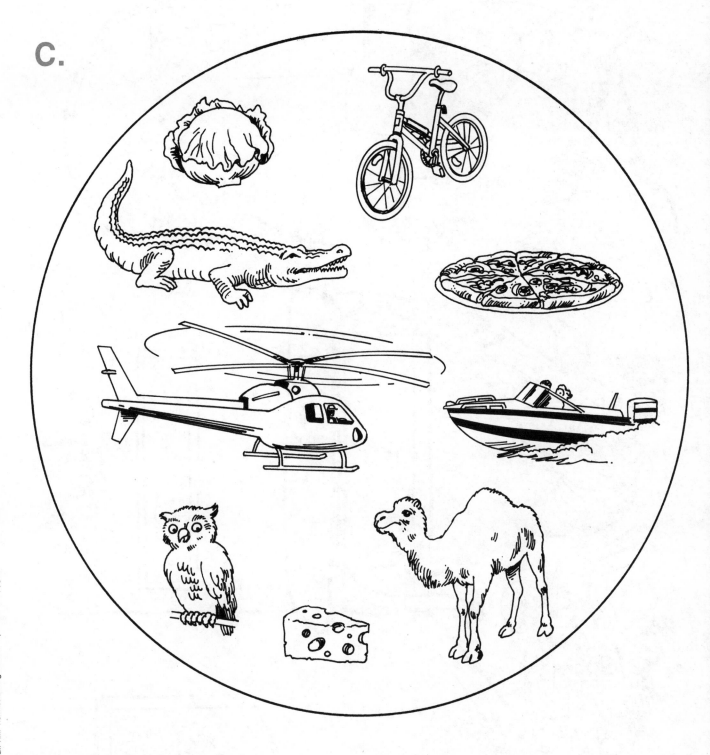

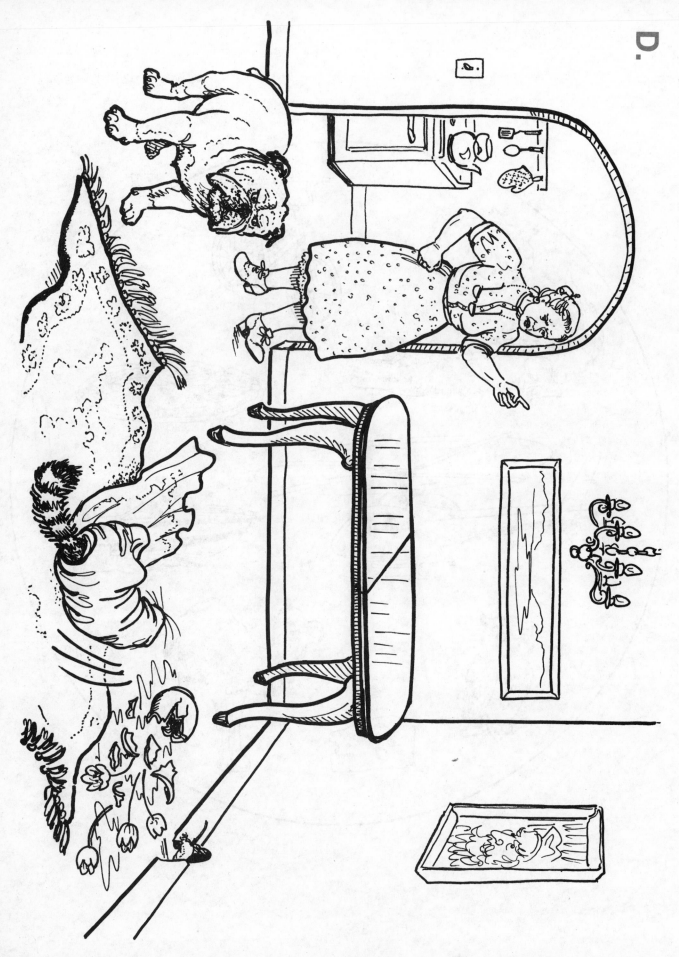

A.

B.

 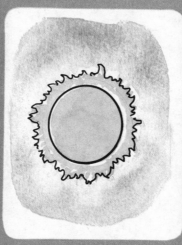 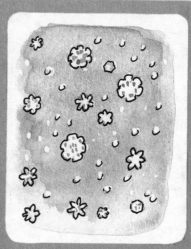

C.

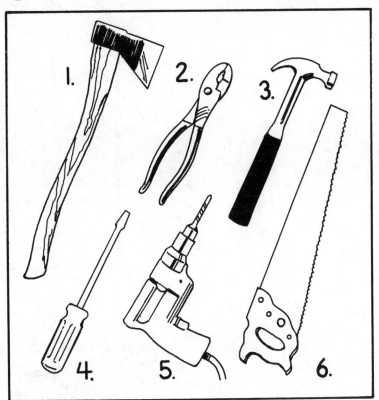

1. 2. 3.
4. 5. 6.

D.

Test Score

A.

1. true   false
2. true   false
3. true   false

4. true   false
5. true   false

B.

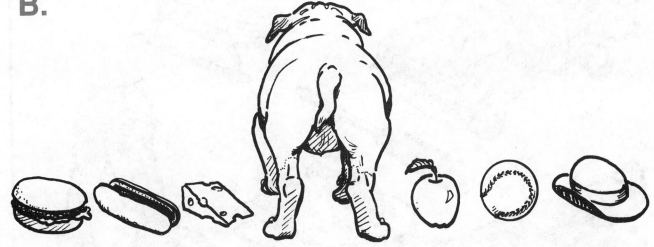

1. true   false
2. true   false
3. true   false

4. true   false
5. true   false

A.

B.

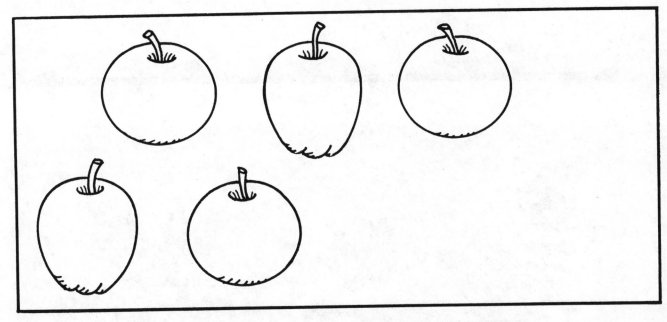

1. true   false   3. true   false

2. true   false   4. true   false

C.

D.

A.

B.

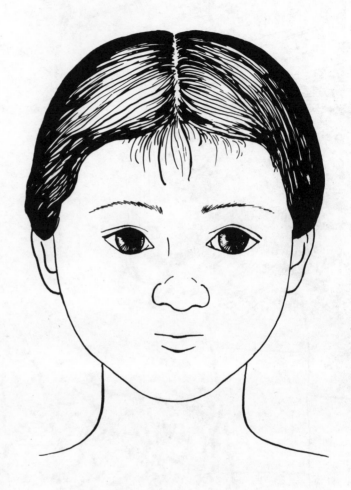

1. true false
2. true false
3. true false
4. true false

C.

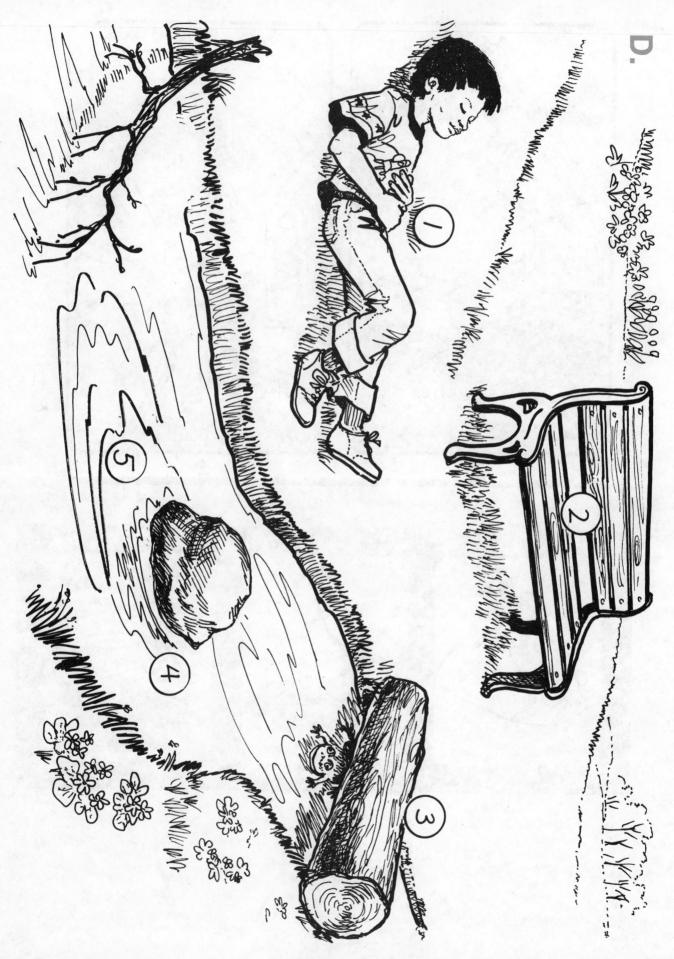

A.

1. true   false
2. true   false
3. true   false

B.

C.

 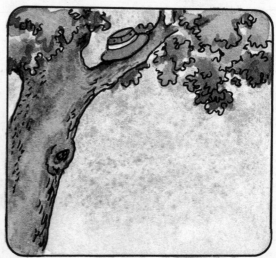

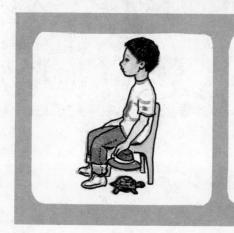  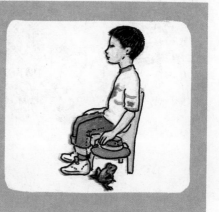

D.

E.

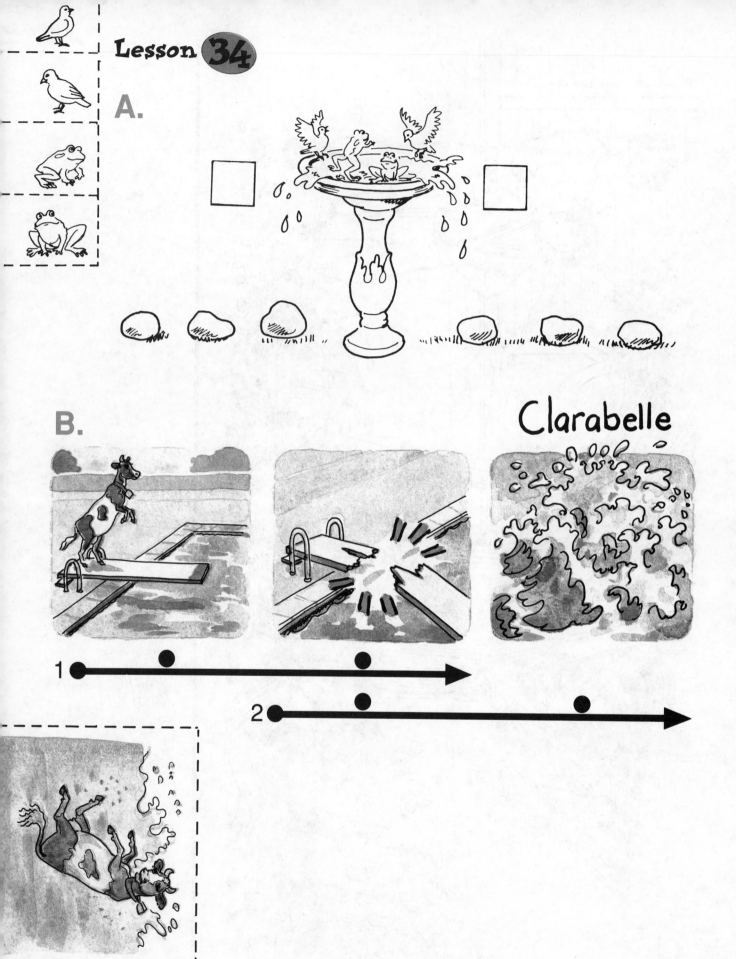

A.

B.

Clarabelle

1

2

C.

A.

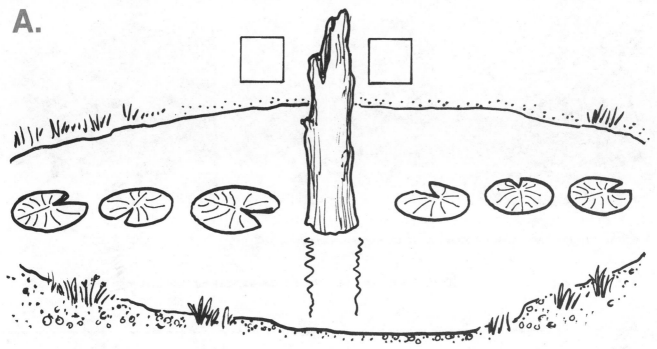

B.

1. true   false   3. true   false

2. true   false   4. true   false

C.

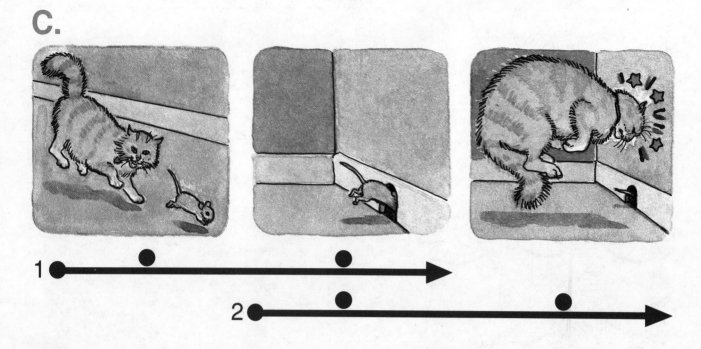

1

2

D.

E.